Fun With Mud

by Deborah Schecter

W9-CDR-868

ISBN-13: 978-0-545-25705-3 / ISBN-10: 0-545-25705-0

Illustrated by Anne Kennedy
Designed by Maria Lilja • Colored by Ka-Yeon Kim-Li
Copyright © 2010 by Deborah Schecter

SCHOLASTIC

Mud cookies.

Mud cakes.

Mud pies.

Mud donuts.

Mud muffins.

Mud bread.

Bake sale!